BRYCE CANYON
NATIONAL PARK
ACTIVITY BOOK

PUZZLES, MAZES, GAMES, AND MORE ABOUT
BRYCE CANYON NATIONAL PARK

NATIONAL PARKS ACTIVITIES SERIES

BRYCE CANYON NATIONAL PARK ACTIVITY BOOK

Copyright 2021
Published by Little Bison Press

The author acknowledges that the land on which Bryce Canyon National Park is located are the traditional lands of Pueblos, Southern Paiute, and Ute Tribes.

LITTLE BISON
Press

For more free national parks activities, visit
www.littlebisonpress.com

About Bryce Canyon National Park

Bryce Canyon National Park is located in the state of Utah. The park's namesake is Bryce Canyon which, despite its name, is not an actual canyon but a series of natural stone amphitheaters.

This park is famous for having spire-shaped rock formations, also known as red rock hoodoos. Bryce Canyon has the largest collection of hoodoos in the world. These formations were shaped by erosion, a natural process where soil and rock are removed by wind or water. Hoodoos erode about 2-4 feet per century, so they won't last forever.

People often visit Bryce Canyon for stargazing opportunities. The high elevation, clean air, and remote location add up to some of the darkest skies in the US. If the weather is clear and the moon is right, you can view thousands of stars across the sky.

Bryce Canyon National Park is **famous for**:
- dark skies perfect for stargazing
- Mormon pioneers
- hoodoos

Hey, I'm Parker!

I'm the only snail in history to visit every National Park in the United States! Come join me on my adventures in Bryce Canyon National Park.

Throughout this book, we will learn about the history of the park, the animals and plants that live here, and things to do if you ever visit in person. This book is also full of games and activities!

Last but not least, I am hidden 9 times on different pages. See how many times you can find me. This page doesn't count!

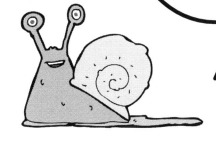

Bryce Canyon Bingo

Let's play bingo! Cross off each box you are able to during your visit to the national park. Try to get a bingo down, across, or diagonally. If you can't visit the park, use the bingo board to plan your perfect trip.

Pick out some activities you would want to do during your visit. What would you do first? How long would you spend there? What animals would you try to see?

DRINK EXTRA WATER	SEE HOODOOS	IDENTIFY A TREE	TAKE A PICTURE AT AN OVERLOOK	WATCH A MOVIE AT THE VISITORS CENTER
GO FOR A HIKE	LEARN ABOUT THE INDIGENOUS PEOPLE WHO LIVE IN THIS AREA	WITNESS A SUNRISE OR SUNSET	OBSERVE THE NIGHT SKIES	GO STARGAZING
HEAR A BIRD CALL	GO ON THE 38 MILE SCENIC DRIVE	FREE SPACE	LEARN ABOUT THE MORMON PIONEERS	VISIT A RANGER STATION
PICK UP TEN PIECES OF TRASH	GO CAMPING	SEE A PRAIRIE DOG	HIKE ALONG THE RIM TRAIL	SPOT A BIRD OF PREY
LEARN ABOUT THE GEOLOGY OF THE ROCKS	SEE SOMEONE RIDING A HORSE	HAVE A PICNIC	SPOT SOME ANIMAL TRACKS	PARTICIPATE IN A RANGER-LED ACTIVITY

The National Park Logo

The National Park System has over 400 units in the US. Just like Bryce Canyon National Park, each location is unique or special in some way. The areas include other national parks, historic sites, monuments, seashores, and other recreation areas.

Each element of the National Park emblem represents something that the National Park Service protects. Fill in each blank below to show what each symbol represents.

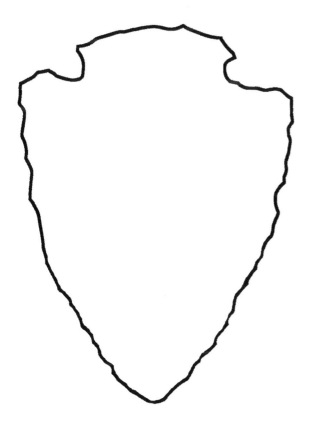

```
WORD BANK:

MOUNTAINS, ARROWHEAD, BISON,
SEQUOIA TREE, WATER
```

This represents all plants: _____

This represents all animals: _____

This represents the landscapes: _____

This represents the waters protected by the park service: _____

This represents the historical and archeological values: _____

Now it's your turn! Pretend you are designing a new national park. Add elements to the design that represent the things your park protects.

What is the name of your park?

Describe why you included the symbols that you chose. What do they mean?

Things to Do Jumble

Unscramble the letters to uncover activities you can do while in Bryce Canyon National Park. Hint: each one ends in -ing.

1. SARTGZA ⬜⬜⬜⬜⬜⬜⬜ING

2. KHI ⬜⬜⬜ING

3. RIBD ⬜⬜⬜⬜ING

4. MAPC ⬜⬜⬜⬜ING

5. KINICPC ⬜⬜⬜⬜⬜⬜⬜ING

6. ESSTEIGH ⬜⬜⬜⬜⬜⬜⬜⬜ING

7. RABEHOSRCKID ⬜⬜⬜⬜⬜⬜⬜⬜⬜⬜⬜⬜ING

Word Bank

birding
reading
camping
stargazing
horseback riding
hiking
hunting
singing
yelling
sightseeing
picnicking

What is a Hoodoo?

A hoodoo is a pinnacle, spire, or odd-shaped rock left standing by the forces of erosion. Draw a hoodoo in the box below. It can be one you saw in the park, or one from your imagination. To show how tall the hoodoo is, draw a person or an animal next to it.

Go Birdwatching at Sunset Point

start here

DID YOU KNOW?
Bryce Canyon National Park is home to several birds of prey, including eagles, hawks, and owls. Birds of prey are birds that hunt other animals for food.

Camping Packing List

What should you take with you when you go camping? Pretend you are in charge of your family camping trip. Make a list of what you would need to be safe and comfortable on an overnight excursion. Some considerations are listed on the side.

1.
2.
3.
4.
5.
6.
7.
8.
9.
10.
11.
12.
13.
14.
15.
16.

- What will you eat at every meal?

- What will the weather be like?

- Where will you sleep?

- What will you do during your free time?

- How luxurious do you want camp to be?

- How will you cook?

- How will you see at night?

- How will you dispose of trash?

- What might you need in case of emergencies?

Bryce Canyon National Park

Visitor's Log

Date:

Season:

Who I went with:

Which entrance:

How was your experience? Write a few sentences about your trip. Where did you stay? What did you do? What was your favorite activity? If you haven't visited the park yet, write a paragraph pretending that you did.

STAMPS

Many national parks and monuments have cancellation stamps for visitors to use. These rubber stamps record the date and location that you visited. Many people collect the markings as a free souvenir. Check with a ranger to see where you can find a stamp during your visit. If you aren't able to find one, you can draw your own.

Where is the Park?

Bryce Canyon National Park is in the northwest United States. It is located in Utah. The nickname for Utah is the Beehive State. Try and find Utah below!

Utah

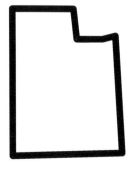

Look at the shape of Utah. Can you find it on the map? If you are from the US, can you find your home state? Color Utah red. Put a star on the map where you live.

Connect the Dots #1

Connect the dots to figure out what this tiny critter is. There are three types of these that live in Bryce Canyon National Park.

Their heart rate can reach as high as 1,260 beats per minute and a breathing rate of 250 breaths per minute. Have you ever measured your breathing rate? Ask a friend or family member to set a timer for 60 seconds. Once they say "go," try to breathe normally. Count each breath until they say "stop." How do your breaths per minute compare to hummingbirds?

_____

_____

Whiptail lizards are relatively small lizards with long tails. All whiptails are female as they reproduce asexually.

Cottontail rabbits typically have a stubby white-colored tail. Birds of prey are one of the most common predators of cottontails.

Who Lives in Bryce Canyon?

Below are 9 plants and animals that live in the park. Use the word bank to fill in the clues below. Pay attention to how many letters each word has to see where it fits.

◻◻◻◻◻◻■ S ◻◻◻

◻ O ◻◻◻◻

◻ U ◻◻■◻◻◻

◻◻◻ T ◻◻◻◻◻

◻ H ◻◻◻◻◻

◻◻◻◻◻◻■ W ◻◻

◻◻◻◻◻◻◻■◻ E ◻◻

◻ S ◻◻◻

◻◻◻◻ T ◻◻◻◻◻

WORD BANK:

OSPREY, WHIPTAIL, CHEATGRASS, GOPHER SNAKE, BOBCAT, CANYON WREN, MULE DEER, PRICKLY PEAR, COTTONTAIL

14

Bighorn sheep are named for the large horns grown by the males of the species. These horns usually reach maximum size when the sheep are 8 to 10 years of age.

Bald Eagles aren't actually bald, but the feathers on their heads are white. The diet of bald eagles consists of fish, other birds, and small mammals.

Common Names
vs.
Scientific Names

A common name of an organism is a name that is based on everyday language. You have heard the common names of plants, animals, and other living things on tv, in books, and at school. Common names can also be referred to as "English" names, popular names, or farmer's names. Common names can vary from place to place. The word for a particular tree may be one thing, but that same tree has a different name in another country. Common names can even vary from region to region, even in the same country.

Scientific names, or Latin names, are given to organisms to make it possible to have uniform names for the same species. Scientific names are in Latin. You may have heard plants or animals referred to by their scientific name or parts of their scientific names. Latin names are also called "binomial nomenclature," which refers to a two-part naming system. The first part of the name – the generic name – refers to the genus to which the species belongs. The second part of the name, the specific name, identifies the species. For example, Tyrannosaurus rex is an example of a widely known scientific name.

American Black Bear

Ursus americanus

COMMON NAME

Bighorn Sheep

Ovis canadensis

LATIN NAME = GENUS + SPECIES

Bighorn Sheep = Ovis canadensis

Black Bear = Ursus americanus

Find the Match!
Common Names and Latin Names

Match the common name to the scientific name for each animal. The first one is done for you. Use clues on the page before and after this one to complete the matches.

Bighorn Sheep   Haliaeetus leucocephalus

Two-needle Piñon   Ursus americanus

Cheatgrass   Pandion haliaetus

American Black Bear   Opuntia engelmannii

Great Horned Owl   Pinus edulis

Bald Eagle   Aspidoscelis uniparens

Osprey   Bubo virginianus

Prickly Pear   Ovis canadensis

Whiptail   Bromus tectorum

Bald Eagle

Haliaeetus leucocephalus

Osprey
Pandion haliaetus

Two-needle Piñon
Pinus edulis

Great Horned Owl
Bubo virginianus

Some plants and animals that live in Utah

Prickly Pear
Opuntia engelmannii

Cheatgrass
Bromus tectorum

Whiptail
Aspidoscelis uniparens

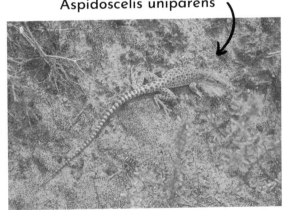

Rock Scavenger Hunt

Pay close attention to the things beneath your feet. If you visit Bryce Canyon National Park, you will see all sorts of rocks, both big and small. Go on a rock hunt! You may have to get close to the ground and focus carefully to be able to find all the rocks on this list.

☐ A sharp rock

☐ A flat rock

☐ A round rock

☐ A rectangular rock

☐ A dull rock

☐ A rock with stripes

☐ A multicolored rock

☐ A smooth rock

☐ A small rock

☐ A huge rock

☐ A rough rock

☐ A shiny rock

☐ A rock with speckles

☐ A rock with only one color

Compare two rocks that look very different from each other.
What makes them different? Think about their size, their shape, their texture, and their color.
Do they have any similarities?

_____

_____

The Ten Essentials

The ten essentials are a list of things that are important to have when you go for longer hikes. If you go on a hike to the backcountry, it is especially important that you have everything you need in case of an emergency. If you get lost or something unforeseen happens, it is good to be prepared to survive until help finds you.

The ten essentials list was developed in the 1930s by an outdoors group called the Mountaineers. Over time and technological advancements, this list has evolved. Can you identify all the things on the current list? Circle each of the "essentials" and cross out everything that doesn't make the cut.

fire: matches, lighter, tinder, and/or stove	a pint of milk	extra money	headlamp plus extra batteries	extra clothes
extra water	a dog	Polaroid camera	bug net	lightweight games, such as a deck of cards
extra food	a roll of duct tape	shelter	sun protection such as sunglasses, sun-protective clothes and sunscreen	knife, plus a gear repair kit
a mirror	navigation: map, compass, altimeter, GPS device, or satellite messenger	first aid kit	extra flip-flops	entertainment such as video games or books

Backcountry - a remote undeveloped rural area.

Help Protect
Endangered Species

Bryce Canyon National Park is home to several animals on the endangered species list. Create a magazine article that would encourage people to help protect an endangered species.

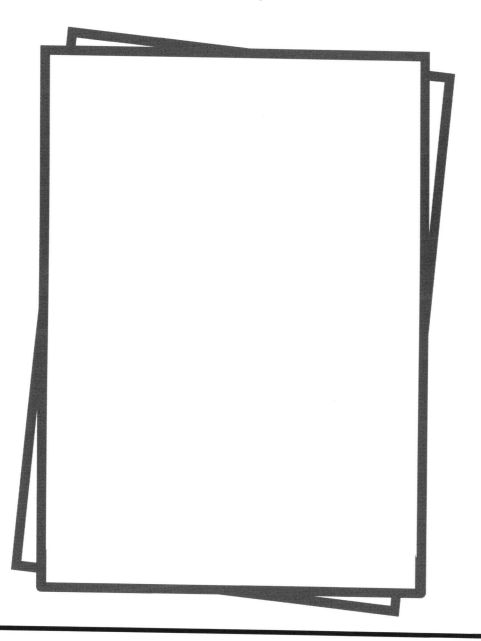

Connect the Dots #2

While California Condors are rare, they can occasionally be spotted in Bryce Canyon. They have the largest wingspan of any bird in North America: up to 11 feet! A wingspan is the distance from one wingtip to the other wingtip. There is a similar measurement for humans. This is called an arm span, since humans don't have wings.

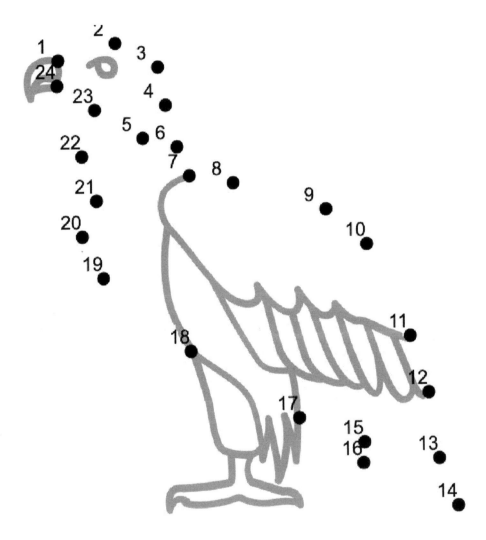

Do you know how long your arm span is? You can have a friend or family member help you measure it. Stand with your back against a wall and stretch out your arms. With a measuring tape, measure from the tip of your left middle finger to the tip of your right middle finger. How long is your arm span? Is it longer or shorter than the wingspan of a California Condor?

_____

_____

LISTEN CAREFULLY

Visitors to Bryce Canyon National Park may hear different noises than those they hear at home. Try this activity to experience this for yourself!

First, find a place outside where it is comfortable to sit or stand for a few minutes. You can do this by yourself or with a friend or family member. Once you have a good spot, close your eyes and listen. Be quiet for one minute and pay attention to what you are hearing. List some of the sounds you have heard in one of the two boxes below:

NATURAL SOUNDS
MADE BY ANIMALS, THE WIND, TREES OR PLANTS, ETC

HUMAN-MADE SOUNDS
MADE BY PEOPLE, MACHINES, ETC

ONCE YOU ARE BACK AT HOME, TRY REPEATING YOUR EXPERIMENT:

NATURAL SOUNDS
MADE BY ANIMALS, THE WIND, TREES OR PLANTS, ETC

HUMAN-MADE SOUNDS
MADE BY PEOPLE, MACHINES, ETC

WHERE DID YOU HEAR MORE NATURAL SOUNDS?

WHERE DID YOU HEAR MORE HUMAN SOUNDS?

Snail Mail

Design a postcard to send to a friend or family member. Who do you want to tell about Bryce Canyon National Park? In the first template, write your message. In the second template, create a design for the front of the postcard. You could show something you saw, something you did, or something you want to do in the national park.

Postcard

Bryce Canyon Word Search

Words may be horizontal, vertical, diagonal, or
they might even be backwards!

1. hoodoo
2. red rock
3. thors hammer
4. dark sky
5. erosion
6. mormon
7. pioneers
8. canyons
9. Paiute
10. cenozoic
11. amphitheater
12. rainbow point
13. pueblo
14. arches
15. pinyon
16. under the rim
17. weathering
18. snow

```
U M A M P H I T H E A T E R M
E N I E P E T U I A P R O A R
O L D F A I H S R E E N O I P
S O A E O D O C L T R G T N O
A D R C R Y R T E S O N A B S
V S K S L T S H B I S I N O E
P N S O V E H S B G I R A W V
E O K A R Y A E E T O E I P E
R Y Y T M O M Y R R N H W O L
K N H U H E M R T I N T S I S
L A R O F E E D R C M A T N A
A C D N O M R O M K H E O T N
R I E W I D I O I F T W P I O
C P B H R S O N N A M C D N Y
H M C E N O Z O I C T N U G N
E S Q U I R R E D R O C K E I
S C R T R A V E R T I N E W P
B O I L P U E B L O E R A D M
```

25

Map Symbol Sudoku

The National Park System makes park maps using symbols instead of words.
They are easily understood and take up way less space on a tiny map.

Trailhead

Cabin

Wildlife

Campground

Complete this symbol sudoku puzzle. Fill each square with one of the symbols. Each one can appear only once in each row, column, and mini 2x2 grid. Each symbol means something, so you can write what the symbol represents instead of drawing the symbols if you prefer.

Staying Safe in the Sun

It is important to take precautions to stay safe outdoors, especially when it is very hot outside. When someone gets overheated or dehydrated, they may feel sick or even require medical attention.

Use the cryptogram below to decode three tips on how to prevent heat-related illnesses. You may need to do some math to figure out the answers.

T _ _ _   _ _ _ _ _ _   _ _   _ _ _ _
12 5 12/2 50   30 21 50 5 2x3 36   3x4 27   21 50 6x6 12

_ _   _ _ _   _ _ _ _ _ .
99 10   15-3 4 50   36 7-3 5 1 50

_ _ _ _   H _ _ _ _ _ _ _   _ _
36 12 1x5 18   4 2x9 1 21 5 12 50 8-7   30 18

_ _ _ _ _ _ _ _   _ _ _ _   _ _   _ _ _ _ _ .
1 21 99 10 6 33x3 10 75   35 3x9 12 36   27 5x5   18/2 5 12 50 21

_ _ A _   _ _ _ _ _ _ _ _ _   _ _ _
9 50 12-7 21   36 3 10 36 15 21 5x10 50 10   5 10 12-11

_ _ _ - _ _ _ _ _ _ _ _ _
36 3 10   8 7x3 27 12 50 15 9+3 99 80 50

_ _ _ _ _ I N G .
15 35 27 12 2x2 99 10 75

a	b	c	d	e	f	g	h	i	j	k	l	m	n	o
5	30	15	1	50	25	75	4	99	20	6	35	49	10	27

p	q	r	s	t	u	v	w	x	y	z
8	16	21	36	12	3	80	9	40	18	7

The Perfect Picnic Spot

Fill in the blanks on this page without looking at the full story. Once you have each line filled out, use the words you've chosen to complete the story on the next page.

EMOTION _

FOOD _

SOMETHING SWEET _

STORE _

MODE OF TRANSPORTATION _ _ _ _ _ _ _ _ _ _ _ _ _ _ _

NOUN _

SOMETHING ALIVE _

SAUCE _

PLURAL VEGETABLES _ _ _ _ _ _ _ _ _ _ _ _ _ _ _ _ _ _

ADJECTIVE _

PLURAL BODY PART _ _ _ _ _ _ _ _ _ _ _ _ _ _ _ _ _ _ _

ANIMAL _

PLURAL FRUIT _

PLACE _

SOMETHING TALL _ _ _ _ _ _ _ _ _ _ _ _ _ _ _ _ _ _ _

COLOR _

ADJECTIVE _

NOUN _

A DIFFERENT ANIMAL _ _ _ _ _ _ _ _ _ _ _ _ _ _ _ _ _

FAMILY MEMBER #1 _ _ _ _ _ _ _ _ _ _ _ _ _ _ _ _ _ _

FAMILY MEMBER #2 _ _ _ _ _ _ _ _ _ _ _ _ _ _ _ _ _ _

VERB THAT ENDS IN -ING _ _ _ _ _ _ _ _ _ _ _ _ _ _ _

A DIFFERENT FOOD _ _ _ _ _ _ _ _ _ _ _ _ _ _ _ _ _ _ _

The Perfect Picnic Spot

Use the words from the previous page to complete a silly story.

When my family suggested having our lunch at the Rainbow Point picnic area, I

was _ _ _ _ _ _ _ _. I love eating my _ _ _ _ _ _ outside! I knew we had picked up a
     EMOTION   FOOD

box of _ _ _ _ _ _ from the _ _ _ _ _ _ _ _ for after lunch, my favorite. We drove up
       SOMETHING SWEET   STORE

to the area and I jumped out of the _ _ _ _ _ _ _ _. "I will find the perfect spot for
                                     MODE OF TRANSPORTATION

a picnic!" I grabbed a _ _ _ _ _ _ for us to sit on, and I ran off. I passed a picnic
                        NOUN

table, but it was covered with _ _ _ _ _ _ _ so we couldn't sit there. The next picnic
                               SOMETHING ALIVE

table looked okay, but there were smears of _ _ _ _ _ _ and pieces of _ _ _ _ _ _ _ _
                                            SAUCE   PLURAL VEGETABLES

everywhere. The people that were there before must have been _ _ _ _ _ _! I
                                                              ADJECTIVE

gritted my _ _ _ _ _ _ _ together and kept walking down the path, determined to
           PLURAL BODY PART

find the perfect spot. I wanted a table with a good view of the plateau. Why

was this so hard? If we were lucky, I might even get to see _ _ _ _ _ _ eating some
                                                            ANIMAL

_ _ _ _ _ _ on the cliffside. They don't have those in _ _ _ _ _ _ _, where I am from. I
PLURAL FRUIT   PLACE

walked down a little hill and there it was, the perfect spot! The trees towered

overhead and looked as tall as _ _ _ _ _ _ _. The patch of grass was a beautiful
                               SOMETHING TALL

_ _ _ _ _ _ color. The _ _ _ _ _ _ flowers were growing on
COLOR   ADJECTIVE

the side of a _ _ _ _ _ _ _. I looked across the plateau edge and even saw a
              NOUN

_ _ _ _ _ _ _ _ on the edge of a rock. I looked back to see my _ _ _ _ _ _ _ _ _ and
DIFFERENT ANIMAL   FAMILY MEMBER #1

_ _ _ _ _ _ _ _ _ _ _ _ _ _ _ _ _ a picnic basket. "I hope you brought plenty of
FAMILY MEMBER #2   VERB THAT ENDS IN ING

_ _ _ _ _ _ _, I'm starving!"
A DIFFERENT FOOD

29

Hike to a Hoodoo

start here

DID YOU KNOW?
Hoodoos are tall, thin rocks that protrude from the bottom of a basin. Have you seen any in the park?

Utah Word Search

Words may be horizontal, vertical, diagonal,
or they might even be backwards!

1. osprey
2. Utah
3. southwest
4. canyon
5. explore
6. reptile
7. dry
8. desert
9. hiking
10. rocks
11. Salt Lake City
12. geology
13. pinyon pine
14. pine nuts
15. cliffs
16. beehive
17. arid
18. cactus

```
C W S O U T H W E S T L O W K
H T A A K I L O C H E L A N J
T G E O L O G Y C C L B A P E
P M P A Y T R S C E R L H L X
I I A D R A L L O E I U I A P
N O N D D I R A D C T T K S L
Y E S E E H E K K B P R I C O
O L B A N U I E G E N E N A R
N E H S G U L O R E C D G D E
P C I C A C T U S H P I O E A
I T A L C H I S O I K E T S N
N R N I K O E I O V O K I Y E
E I O F H Z D E S E R T L G W
J C G F L O V E P O O R V E H
N I L S K H I N R O C K S E A
X T A I A E E G E Z E P R N L
H T D T O E N O Y N A C C I E
U J U O S N E D N Y M A L A Z
```

31

Leave No Trace Quiz

Leave No Trace is a concept that helps people make decisions during outdoor recreation that protects the environment. There are seven principles that guide us when we spend time outdoors, whether you are in a national park or not. Are you an expert in Leave No Trace? Take this quiz and find out!

1. How can you plan ahead and prepare to ensure you have the best experience you can in the national park?
    a. Make sure you stop by the ranger station for a map and to ask about current conditions.
    b. Just wing it! You will know the best trail when you see it.
    c. Stick to your plan, even if conditions change. You traveled a long way to get here, and you should stick to your plan.
2. What is an example of traveling on a durable surface?
    a. Walking only on the designated path.
    b. Walking on the grass that borders the trail if the trail is very muddy.
    c. Taking a shortcut if you can find one because it means you will be walking less.
3. Why should you dispose of waste properly?
    a. You don't need to. Park rangers love to pick up the trash you leave behind.
    b. You should actually leave your leftovers behind, because animals will eat them. It is important to make sure they aren't hungry.
    c. So that other peoples' experiences of the park are not impacted by you leaving your waste behind.
4. How can you best follow the concept "leave what you find?"
    a. Take only a small rock or leaf to remember your trip.
    b. Take pictures, but leave any physical items where they are.
    c. Leave everything you find, unless it may be rare like an arrowhead, then it is okay to take.
5. What is not a good example of minimizing campfire impacts?
    a. Only having a campfire in a pre-existing campfire ring.
    b. Checking in with current conditions when you consider making a campfire.
    c. Building a new campfire ring in a location that has a better view.
6. What is a poor example of respecting wildlife?
    a. Building squirrel houses out of rocks so the squirrels have a place to live.
    b. Stay far away from wildlife and give them plenty of space.
    c. Reminding your grown-ups not to drive too fast in animal habitats while visiting the park.
7. How can you show consideration of other visitors?
    a. Play music on your speaker so other people at the campground can enjoy it.
    b. Wear headphones on the trail if you choose to listen to music.
    c. Make sure to yell "Hello!" to every animal you see at top volume.

Park Poetry

America's parks inspire art of all kinds. Painters, sculptors, photographers, writers, and artists of all mediums have taken inspiration from natural beauty. They have turned their inspiration into great works.

Use this space to write your own poem about the park. Think about what you have experienced or seen. Use descriptive language to create an acrostic poem. This type of poem has the first letter of each line spell out another word. Create an acrostic that spells out the word "Utah."

U _____

T _____

A _____

H _____

Under big sky

Towering rocks

All around me

Hot dry land

Up in the air

Top predator

A bird so ferocious

Hovering over its prey

Draw A Meal

Imagine you've been adventuring all day and now it's time to go back to camp for the night. You are hungry!

Draw the meal that you will cook over the campfire.

Navigate Through the Hoodoo

start here →

Bryce Canyon has the largest concentration of hoodoos in the world. These rock formations have been here long before you were born and before this place was established as a park.

Formations like fins, windows, and hoodoos are created by natural forces called weathering and erosion. Weathering and erosion are slow, occurring over thousands and millions of years.

Stacking Rocks

Have you ever seen stacks of rocks while hiking in national parks? Do you know what they are or what they mean? These rock piles are called cairns and often mark hiking routes in parks. Every park has a different way to maintain trails and cairns. However, they all have the same rule: If you come across a cairn, do not disturb it!

Color the cairn and the rules to remember.

1. Do not tamper with cairns.

If a cairn is tampered with or an unauthorized one is built, then future visitors may become disoriented or even lost.

2. Do not build unauthorized cairns.

Moving rocks disturbs the soil and makes the area more prone to erosion. Disturbing rocks can disturb fragile plants.

3. Do not add to existing cairns.

Authorized cairns are carefully designed. Adding to them can actually cause them to collapse.

Decoding Using American Sign Language

American Sign Language, also called ASL for short, is a language that many Deaf people or people who are hard of hearing use to communicate. People use ASL to communicate with their hands. Did you know people from all over the country and world travel to national parks? You may hear people speaking other languages. You might also see people using ASL. Use the American Manual Alphabet chart to decode some national parks facts.

This was the first national park to be established:

_ _ _ _ _ _ _ _ _ _

This is the biggest national park in the US:

_ _ _ _ _ _ _ _ _

_ _ . _ _ _ _

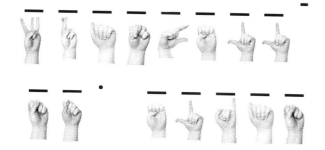

This is the most visited national park:

_ _ _ _ _ _ _ _ _ _

_ _ _ _ _ _ _ _

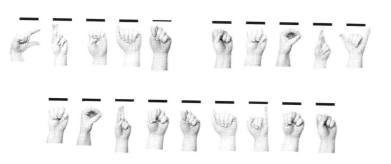

Hint: Pay close attention to
the position of the thumb!

Try it! Using the chart, try to make the letters of the alphabet with your hand. What is the hardest letter to make? Can you spell out your name? Show a friend or family member and have them watch you spell out the name of the national park you are in.

Go Horseback Riding in the Bryce Amphitheater

Help find the horse's lost shoe!

start here →

DID YOU KNOW?

Horseback riding is a popular activity in Bryce Canyon National Park. There are many trails that you can take horses for day trips.

Prairie Dog Digs

Prairie dog colonies or "towns" are made up of tunnels 3 to 6 feet below ground and about 15 feet long. These burrows usually include several distinct chambers inhabited by a coterie, or group, of prairie dogs. These coteries work together to protect the group from predators such as coyotes, badgers, rattlesnakes, and birds of prey. Prairie dog burrows have areas dug out for raising babies, sleeping, and even toilets. They also feature dugouts near the exits, so the prairie dogs can listen to potential predators outside.

Using your knowledge of prairie dog habitat, draw your own version of a prairie dog burrow. Your drawing should include at least 3 different chambers, a coterie with at least 4 prairie dogs, and one potential predator waiting on the surface.

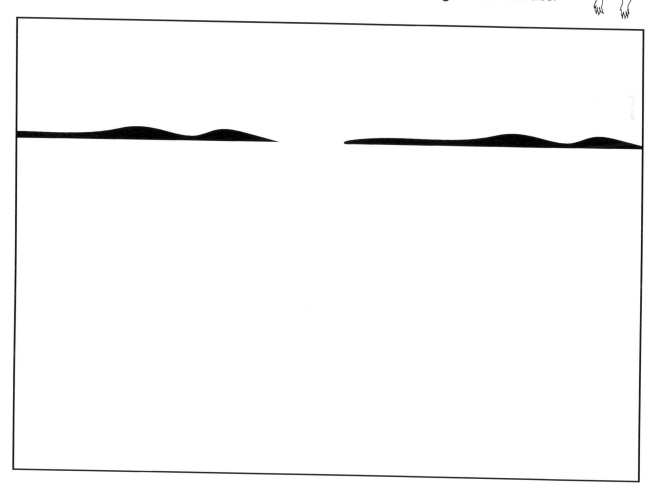

Which predator of the Utah Prairie Dog did you draw? Do you think it will be able to successfully hunt any members of your coterie?

_____

_____

_____

A Hike to Mossy Cave

Fill in the blanks on this page without looking at the full story. Once you have each line filled out, use the words you've chosen to complete the story on the next page.

ADJECTIVE _____

SOMETHING TO EAT _____

SOMETHING TO DRINK _____

NOUN _____

ARTICLE OF CLOTHING _____

BODY PART _____

VERB _____

ANIMAL _____

SAME TYPE OF FOOD _____

ADJECTIVE _____

SAME ANIMAL _____

VERB THAT ENDS IN "ED" _____

NUMBER _____

A DIFFERENT NUMBER _____

SOMETHING THAT FLIES _____

LIGHT SOURCE _____

PLURAL NOUN _____

FAMILY MEMBER _____

YOUR NICKNAME _____

A Hike to Mossy Cave

Use the words from the previous page to complete a silly story.

I went for a hike to Mossy Cave today. In my favorite _ _ _ _ _ _ _ backpack, I
                                                        ADJECTIVE

made sure to pack a map so I wouldn't get lost. I also threw in an extra

_ _ _ _ _ _ _ _ _ _ _ just in case I got hungry and a bottle of _ _ _ _ _ _ _ _ _ _ _. I put
SOMETHING TO EAT   SOMETHING TO DRINK

on my _ _ _ _ _ _ _ _ _ _ spray, and I tied a _ _ _ _ _ _ _ _ _ _ _ _ around my
        NOUN   ARTICLE OF CLOTHING

_ _ _ _ _ _ _ _ _, in case it gets chilly. I started to _ _ _ _ _ _ down the path. As
BODY PART   VERB

soon as I turned the corner, I came face to face with a(n) _ _ _ _ _ _ _ _. I think
                                                          ANIMAL

it was as startled as I was! What should I do? I had to think fast! Should I

give it some of my _ _ _ _ _ _ _ _ _ _ _? No. I had to remember what the
                   SAME TYPE OF FOOD

_ _ _ _ _ _ _ ranger told me: "If you see one, back away slowly and try not to
ADJECTIVE

scare it." Soon enough, the _ _ _ _ _ _ _ _ _ _ _ _ _ _ _ _ _ _ _ _ away. The coast
                           SAME ANIMAL   VERB THAT ENDS IN ED

was clear. _ _ _ _ _ _ hours later, I finally got to the lookout. I felt like I could
           NUMBER

see for a _ _ _ _ _ _ miles. I took a picture of a _ _ _ _ _ _ _ _ so I could always
          A DIFFERENT NUMBER   NOUN

remember this moment. As I was putting my camera away, a _ _ _ _ _ _ _ _ _
                                                          SOMETHING THAT FLIES

flew by, reminding me that it was almost nighttime. I turned on my

_ _ _ _ _ _ _ _ _ _ and headed back. I could hear the _ _ _ _ _ _ _ _ _ _ _ singing their
LIGHT SOURCE   PLURAL INSECT

evening song. Just as I was getting tired, I saw my _ _ _ _ _ _ _ _ _ _ and our tent.
                                                    FAMILY MEMBER

"Welcome back _ _ _ _ _ _ _! How was your hike?"
              NICKNAME

Sound Exploration

Spend a minute or two listening to all of the sounds around you.
Draw your favorite sound.

How did this sound make you feel?

_____

_____

What did you think when you heard this sound?

_____

Let's Go Camping
Word Search

Words may be horizontal, vertical, diagonal, or they might be backwards!

1. tent
2. camp stove
3. sleeping bag
4. bug spray
5. sunscreen
6. map
7. flashlight
8. pillow
9. lantern
10. ice
11. snacks
12. smores
13. water
14. first aid kit
15. chair
16. cards
17. books
18. games
19. trail
20. hat

```
D P P I L L O W D B T E A C I
E O A D P R E A A M B R C A N
P W C A M P S T O V E I H X G
R A H S G E L E B E E D A P S
E L B U G S P R A Y N G I E A
S I A H G C I C N N M E R C N
C W N L A F I R S K O O B F K
M T A E M I L E L H M R W L J
T A P R E A O R E S L B A A B
S M P A S R R T E N T L U S C
C E A I I R C G P E I U J H A
S S N A C K S S I M O K I L R
I J R S F O I S N J R A Q I D
C Y E T L E V E G U O R V G S
E W T A K C A B B S S O H H M
X J N F I R S T A I D K I T T
U A A E S S E N G E T P V A B
C J L I A R T D N A M A H A S
```

All in the Day of a Park Ranger

Park Rangers are hardworking individuals dedicated to protecting our parks, monuments, museums, and more. They take care of the natural and cultural resources for future generations. Rangers also help protect the visitors of the park. Their responsibilities are broad and they work both with the public and behind the scenes.

What have you seen park rangers do? Use your knowledge of the duties of park rangers to fill out a typical daily schedule, listing one activity for each hour. Feel free to make up your own, but some examples of activities are provided on the right. Read carefully! Not all the example activities are befitting a ranger.

6 am	Lead a sunrise hike
7 am	
8 am	
9 am	
10 am	
11 am	
12 pm	Enjoy a lunch break outside
1 pm	
2 pm	
3 pm	
4 pm	Teach visitors about the geology of the hoodoos
5 pm	
6 pm	
7 pm	
8 pm	
9 pm	

- feed the migratory birds
- build trails for visitors to enjoy
- throw rocks off the side of the mountain
- rescue lost hikers
- study animal behavior
- record air quality data
- answer questions at the visitor center
- pick wildflowers
- pick up litter
- share marshmallows with squirrels
- repair handrails
- lead a class on a field trip
- catch frogs or toads and make them race
- lead people on educational hikes
- write articles for the park website
- protect the river from pollution
- remove non-native plants from the park
- study how climate change is affecting the park
- give a talk about mountain lions
- lead a program for campers on prairie dogs

If you were a park ranger, which of the above tasks would you enjoy most?

_____

_____

Draw Yourself as a Park Ranger

The Animals of Bryce Canyon

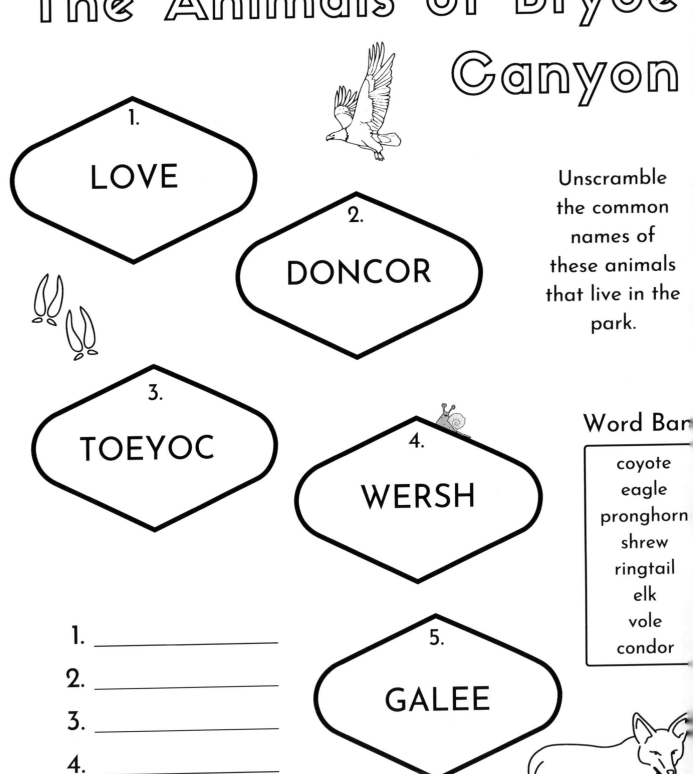

Unscramble the common names of these animals that live in the park.

1. LOVE

2. DONCOR

3. TOEYOC

4. WERSH

5. GALEE

Word Bank

coyote
eagle
pronghorn
shrew
ringtail
elk
vole
condor

1. _____
2. _____
3. _____
4. _____
5. _____

Amphibians

Two species of frogs live in Bryce Canyon National Park. Salamanders live there too. Frogs spend the beginning of their lives as tadpoles. Tadpoles hatch from eggs, usually in springs or pools of water.

Both frogs and salamanders are amphibians. Color the amphibians below.

Build a Bird Nest

Different birds build different kinds of nests where they can lay their eggs and raise their babies.

Draw a nest and some baby birds you might find in Bryce Canyon National Park.

48

Take a Hike

Go for a hike with your friends or family. If you aren't able to visit Bryce Canyon National Park, go for a walk in a park near where you live. Read through the prompts before your walk and finish the activities after you return.

Draw something you saw that moves:

Draw something you saw when you looked up:

Draw something you saw that grows out of the ground:

Draw a picture of your favorite part of the walk:

63 National Parks

How many other national parks have you been to? Which one do you want to visit next? Note that if some of these parks fall on the border of more than one state, you may check it off more than once!

Alaska
- [ ] Denali National Park
- [ ] Gates of the Arctic National Park
- [ ] Glacier Bay National Park
- [ ] Katmai National Park
- [ ] Kenai Fjords National Park
- [ ] Kobuk Valley National Park
- [ ] Lake Clark National Park
- [ ] Wrangell-St. Elias National Park

American Samoa
- [ ] National Park of American Samoa

Arizona
- [ ] Grand Canyon National Park
- [ ] Petrified Forest National Park
- [ ] Saguaro National Park

Arkansas
- [ ] Hot Springs National Park

California
- [ ] Channel Islands National Park
- [ ] Death Valley National Park
- [ ] Joshua Tree National Park
- [ ] Kings Canyon National Park
- [ ] Lassen Volcanic National Park
- [ ] Pinnacles National Park
- [ ] Redwood National Park
- [ ] Sequoia National Park
- [ ] Yosemite National Park

Colorado
- [ ] Black Canyon of the Gunnison National Park
- [ ] Great Sand Dunes National Park
- [ ] Mesa Verde National Park
- [ ] Rocky Mountain National Park

Florida
- [ ] Biscayne National Park
- [ ] Dry Tortugas National Park
- [ ] Everglades National Park

Hawaii
- [ ] Haleakala National Park
- [ ] Hawai'i Volcanoes National Park

Idaho
- [ ] Yellowstone National Park

Kentucky
- [ ] Mammoth Cave National Park

Indiana
- [ ] Indiana Dunes National Park

Maine
- [ ] Acadia National Park

Michigan
- [ ] Isle Royale National Park

Minnesota
- [ ] Voyageurs National Park

Missouri
- [ ] Gateway Arch National Park

Montana
- [ ] Glacier National Park
- [ ] Yellowstone National Park

Nevada
- [ ] Death Valley National Park
- [ ] Great Basin National Park

New Mexico
- [ ] Carlsbad Caverns National Park
- [ ] White Sands National Park

North Dakota
- [ ] Theodore Roosevelt National Park

North Carolina
- [ ] Great Smoky Mountains National Park

Ohio
- [ ] Cuyahoga Valley National Park

Oregon
- [ ] Crater Lake National Park

South Carolina
- [ ] Congaree National Park

South Dakota
- [ ] Badlands National Park
- [ ] Wind Cave National Park

Tennessee
- [ ] Great Smoky Mountains National Park

Texas
- [ ] Big Bend National Park
- [ ] Guadalupe Mountains National Park

Utah
- [ ] Arches National Park
- [ ] Bryce Canyon National Park
- [ ] Canyonlands National Park
- [ ] Capitol Reef National Park
- [ ] Zion National Park

Virgin Islands
- [ ] Virgin Islands National Park

Virginia
- [ ] Shenandoah National Park

Washington
- [ ] Mount Rainier National Park
- [ ] North Cascades National Park
- [ ] Olympic National Park

West Virginia
- [ ] New River Gorge National Park

Wyoming
- [ ] Grand Teton National Park
- [ ] Yellowstone National Park

Other National Parks

Besides Bryce Canyon National Park, there are 62 other diverse and beautiful national parks across the United States. Try your hand at this crossword. If you need help, look at the previous page for some hints.

Down

1. State where Acadia National Park is located
2. This national park has the Spanish word for turtle in it
3. Number of national parks in Alaska
5. This national park has some of the hottest temperatures in the world
6. This national park is the only one in Idaho
7. This toothsome creature can famously be found in Everglades National Park
8. Only president with a national park named for them

Across

4. This state has the most national parks
9. This park has some of the newest land in the US, caused by volcanic eruptions
10. This park has the deepest lake in the United States
11. This color shows up in the name of a national park in California
12. This national park deserves a gold medal

Which National Park Will You Go To Next? Word Search

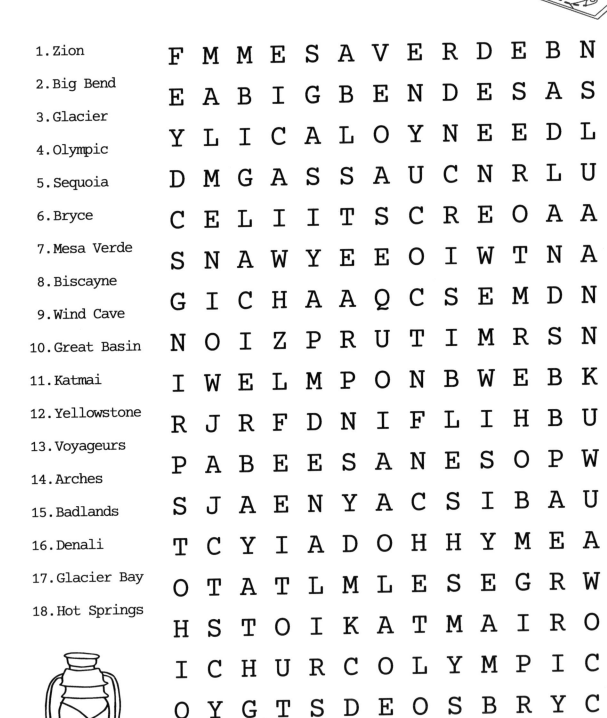

1. Zion
2. Big Bend
3. Glacier
4. Olympic
5. Sequoia
6. Bryce
7. Mesa Verde
8. Biscayne
9. Wind Cave
10. Great Basin
11. Katmai
12. Yellowstone
13. Voyageurs
14. Arches
15. Badlands
16. Denali
17. Glacier Bay
18. Hot Springs

```
F M M E S A V E R D E B N E Y
E A B I G B E N D E S A S E M
Y L I C A L O Y N E E D L T G
D M G A S S A U C N R L U E R
C E L I I T S C R E O A A K E
S N A W Y E E O I W T N A C A
G I C H A A Q C S E M D N S T
N O I Z P R U T I M R S N E B
I W E L M P O N B W E B K H A
R J R F D N I F L I H B U C S
P A B E E S A N E S O P W R I
S J A E N Y A C S I B A U A N
T C Y I A D O H H Y M E A L R
O T A T L M L E S E G R W R J
H S T O I K A T M A I R O P B
I C H U R C O L Y M P I C O U
O Y G T S D E O S B R Y C E T
W I N D C A V E I N R O H E M
```

Field Notes

Spend some time reflecting on your trip to Bryce Canyon National Park. Your field notes will help you remember the things you experienced. Use the space below to write about your day.

While I was at Bryce Canyon National Park...

I saw:

_____

_____

_____

_____

I heard:

_____

_____

_____

I felt:

_____

_____

Draw a picture of your favorite thing in the park.

_____

I wondered:

_____

_____

_____

_____

_____

ANSWER KEY

National Park Emblem Answers

1. This represents all plants: **Sequoia Tree**

2. This represents all animals: **Bison**

3. This represents the landscapes: **Mountains**

4. This represents the waters protected by the park service: **Water**

5. This represents the historical and archeological values: **Arrowhead**

Jumbles Answers

1. STAR GAZING

2. HIKING

3. BIRDING

4. CAMPING

5. PICNICKING

6. SIGHTSEEING

7. HORSEBACK RIDING

Go Birdwatching at Sunset Point

start here

DID YOU KNOW?
Bryce Canyon NP is home to several birds of prey, including eagles, hawks, and owls. Birds of prey are birds that hunt other animals for food.

Answers: Who Lives in Bryce Canyon?

Below are 9 plants and animals that live in the park. Use the word bank to fill in the clues below. Pay attention to how many letters each word has to see where it fits.

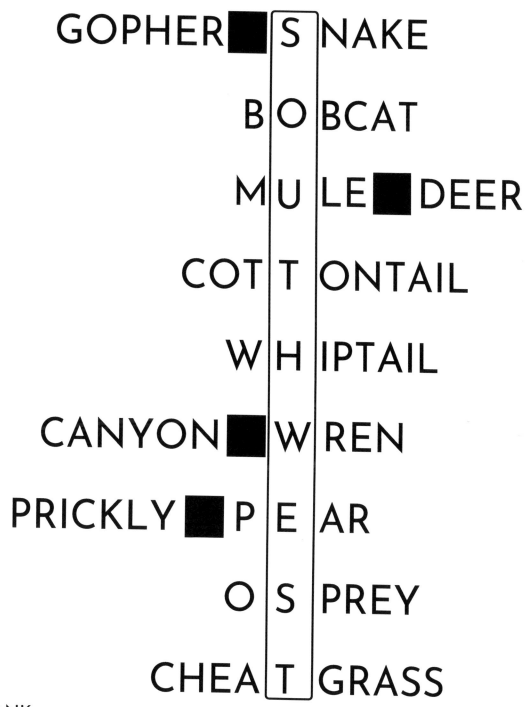

GOPHER ■ S NAKE

B O BCAT

MU LE ■ DEER

COT T ONTAIL

W H IPTAIL

CANYON ■ W REN

PRICKLY ■ P E AR

O S PREY

CHEA T GRASS

WORD BANK:

CHEATGRASS, GOPHER SNAKE, BOBCAT, CANYON WREN, MULE DEER,
PRICKLY PEAR, COTTONTAIL, OSPREY, WHIPTAIL

Find the Match!
Common Names and Latin Names

Match the common name to the scientific name for each animal. The first one is done for you. Use clues on the page before and after this one to complete the matches.

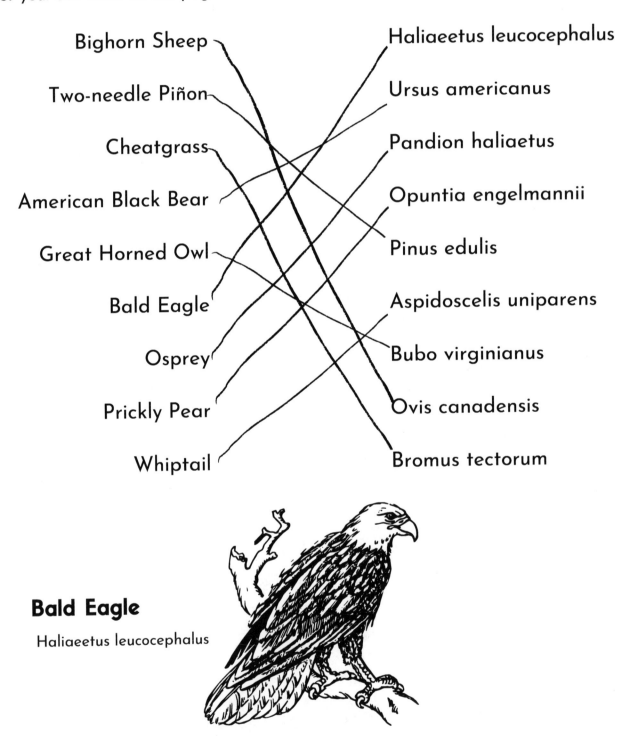

Bighorn Sheep

Two-needle Piñon

Cheatgrass

American Black Bear

Great Horned Owl

Bald Eagle

Osprey

Prickly Pear

Whiptail

Haliaeetus leucocephalus

Ursus americanus

Pandion haliaetus

Opuntia engelmannii

Pinus edulis

Aspidoscelis uniparens

Bubo virginianus

Ovis canadensis

Bromus tectorum

Bald Eagle

Haliaeetus leucocephalus

Answers: The Ten Essentials

The ten essentials are a list of things that are important to have when you go for longer hikes. If you go on a hike to the <u>backcountry</u>, it is especially important that you have everything you need in case of an emergency. If you get lost or something unforeseen happens, it is good to be prepared to survive until help finds you.

The ten essentials list was developed in the 1930s by an outdoors group called the Mountaineers. Over time and technological advancements, this list has evolved. Can you identify all the things on the current list? Circle each of the "essentials" and cross out everything that doesn't make the cut.

Backcountry - a remote undeveloped rural area.

Bryce Canyon Word Search

Words may be horizontal, vertical, diagonal,
and they might even be backwards!

1. hoodoo
2. red rock
3. thors hammer
4. dark sky
5. erosion
6. mormon
7. pioneers
8. canyons
9. Paiute
10. cenozoic
11. amphitheater
12. rainbow point
13. pueblo
14. arches
15. pinyon
16. under the rim
17. weathering
18. snow

```
U M A M P H I T H E A T E R M
E N I E P E T U I A P R O A R
O L D F A I H S R E E N O I P
S O A E O D O C L T R G T N O
A D R C R Y R T E S O N A B S
V S K S L T S H B I S I N O E
P N S O V E H S B G I R A W V
E O K A R Y A E E T O E I P E
R Y Y T M O M Y R R N H W O L
K N H U H E M R T I N T S I S
L A R O F E E D R C M A T N A
A C D N O M R O M K H E O T N
R I E W I D I O I F T W P I O
C P B H R S O N N A M C D N Y
H M C E N O Z O I C T N U G N
E S Q U I R R E D R O C K E I
S C R T R A V E R T I N E W P
  B O I L P U E B L O E R A D M
```

60

Map Symbol Sudoku Anwers

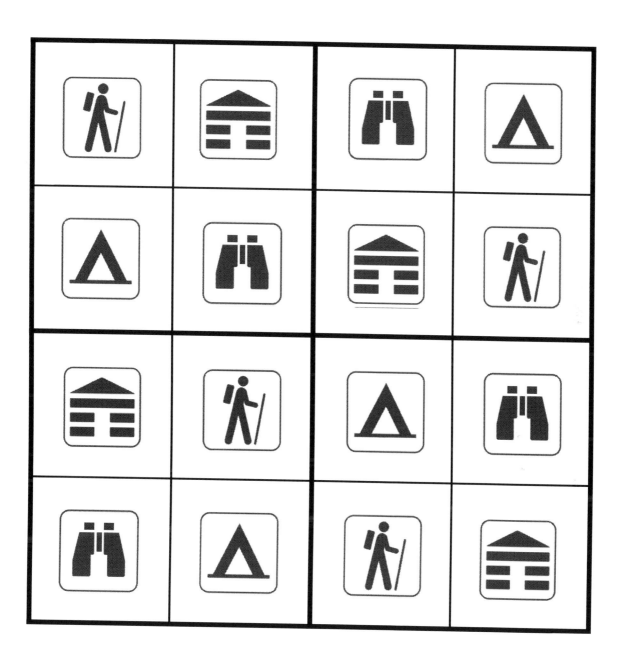

Answer: Hike to a Hoodoo

start here

DID YOU KNOW?
Hoodoos are tall, thin rocks that protrude from the bottom of a basin. Have you seen any in the park?

Utah Word Search

Words may be horizontal, vertical, diagonal,
and they might even be backwards!

1. osprey
2. Utah
3. southwest
4. canyon
5. explore
6. reptile
7. dry
8. desert
9. hiking
10. rocks
11. Salt Lake City
12. geology
13. pinyon pine
14. pine nuts
15. cliffs
16. beehive
17. arid
18. cactus

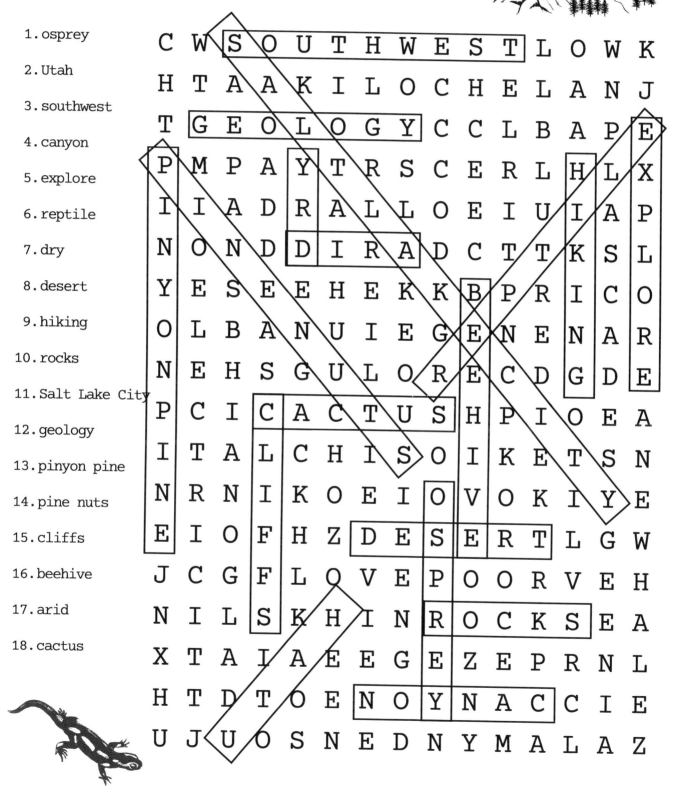

```
C W S O U T H W E S T L O W K
H T A A K I L O C H E L A N J
T G E O L O G Y C C L B A P E
P M P A Y T R S C E R L H L X
I I A D R A L L O E I U I A P
N O N D D I R A D C T T K S L
Y E S E E H E K K B P R I C O
O L B A N U I E G E N E N A R
N E H S G U L O R E C D G D E
P C I C A C T U S H P I O E A
I T A L C H I S O I K E T S N
N R N I K O E I O V O K I Y E
E I O F H Z D E S E R T L G W
J C G F L O V E P O O R V E H
N I L S K H I N R O C K S E A
X T A I A E E G E Z E P R N L
H T D T O E N O Y N A C C I E
U J U O S N E D N Y M A L A Z
```

63

Answers: Leave No Trace Quiz

Leave No Trace is a concept that helps people make decisions during outdoor recreation that protects the environment. There are seven principles that guide us when we spend time outdoors, whether you are in a national park or not. Are you an expert in Leave No Trace? Take this quiz and find out!

1. How can you plan ahead and prepare to ensure you have the best experience you can in the National Park?

    A. Make sure you stop by the ranger station for a map and to ask about current conditions.

2. What is an example of traveling on a durable surface?

    A. Walking only on the designated path.

3. Why should you dispose of waste properly?

    C. So that other peoples' experiences of the park are not impacted by you leaving your waste behind.

4. How can you best follow the concept "leave what you find?"

    B. Take pictures but leave any physical items where they are.

5. What is not a good example of minimizing campfire impacts?

    C. Building a new campfire ring in a location that has a better view.

6. What is a poor example of respecting wildlife?

    A. Building squirrel houses out of rocks from the river so the squirrels have a place to live.

7. How can you show consideration of other visitors?

    B. Wear headphones on the trail if you choose to listen to music.

Navigate Through the Hoodoo

start here →

Bryce Canyon has the largest concentration of hoodoos in the world. These rock formations have been here long before you were born and before this place was established as a park.

Formations like fins, windows, and hoodoos are created by natural forces called weathering and erosion. Weathering and erosion are slow, occurring over thousands and millions of years.

Decoding Using American Sign Language

American Sign Language, also called ASL for short, is a language that many Deaf people or people who are hard of hearing use to communicate. People use ASL to communicate with their hands. Did you know people from all over the country and world travel to national parks? You may hear people speaking other languages. You might also see people using ASL. Use the American Manual Alphabet chart to decode some national parks facts.

This was the first national park to be established:

Y E L L O W S T O N E

This is the biggest national park in the US:

W R A N G E L L -

S T .   E L I A S

This is the most visited national park:

G R E A T   S M O K Y

M O U N T A I N S

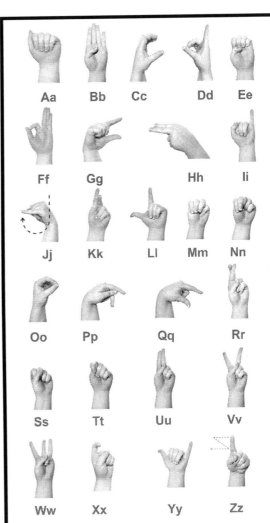

Aa   Bb   Cc   Dd   Ee
Ff   Gg   Hh   Ii
Jj   Kk   Ll   Mm   Nn
Oo   Pp   Qq   Rr
Ss   Tt   Uu   Vv
Ww   Xx   Yy   Zz

Hint: Pay close attention to the position of the thumb!

Try it! Using the chart, try to make the letters of the alphabet with your hand. What is the hardest letter to make? Can you spell out your name? Show a friend or family member and have them watch you spell out the name of the national park you are in.

Go Horseback Riding in the Bryce Amphitheater

Help find the horse's lost shoe!

start here

DID YOU KNOW?

Horseback riding is a popular activity in Bryce Canyon National Park. There are many trails that you can take horses for day trips.

Let's Go Camping
Word Search

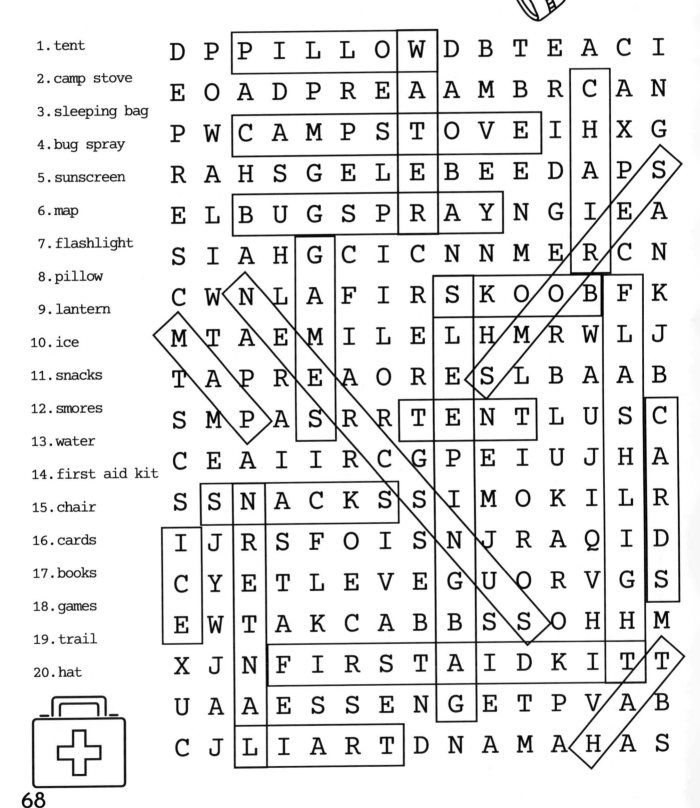

1. tent
2. camp stove
3. sleeping bag
4. bug spray
5. sunscreen
6. map
7. flashlight
8. pillow
9. lantern
10. ice
11. snacks
12. smores
13. water
14. first aid kit
15. chair
16. cards
17. books
18. games
19. trail
20. hat

```
D  P  P  I  L  L  O  W  D  B  T  E  A  C  I
E  O  A  D  P  R  E  A  A  M  B  R  C  A  N
P  W  C  A  M  P  S  T  O  V  E  I  H  X  G
R  A  H  S  G  E  L  E  B  E  E  D  A  P  S
E  L  B  U  G  S  P  R  A  Y  N  G  I  E  A
S  I  A  H  G  C  I  C  N  N  M  E  R  C  N
C  W  N  L  A  F  I  R  S  K  O  O  B  F  K
M  T  A  E  M  I  L  E  L  H  M  R  W  L  J
T  A  P  R  E  A  O  R  E  S  L  B  A  A  B
S  M  P  A  S  R  R  T  E  N  T  L  U  S  C
C  E  A  I  I  R  C  G  P  E  I  U  J  H  A
S  S  N  A  C  K  S  S  I  M  O  K  I  L  R
I  J  R  S  F  O  I  S  N  J  R  A  Q  I  D
C  Y  E  T  L  E  V  E  G  U  O  R  V  G  S
E  W  T  A  K  C  A  B  B  S  S  O  H  H  M
X  J  N  F  I  R  S  T  A  I  D  K  I  T  T
U  A  A  E  S  S  E  N  G  E  T  P  V  A  B
C  J  L  I  A  R  T  D  N  A  M  A  H  A  S
```

All in the Day of a Park Ranger

There are many right answers for this activity, but not all of the provided examples are good activities for a park ranger. In fact, a park ranger's job may include stopping visitors from doing some of these things.

The list below are activities that rangers do not do:

feed the migratory birds

throw rocks off the side of the mountain

pick wildflowers

share marshmallows with squirrels

catch frogs or toads and make them race

The Animals of Bryce Canyon

1. VOLE
2. CONDOR
3. COYOTE
4. SHREW
5. EAGLE

Answers: Other National Parks

Down

1. State where Acadia National Park is located
2. This National Park has the Spanish word for turtle in it
3. Number of National Parks in Alaska
5. This National Park has some of the hottest temperatures in the world
6. This National Park is the only one in Idaho
7. This toothsome creature can famously be found in Everglades National Park
   Only president with a national park named them

Across

4. This state has the most National Parks
9. This park has some of the newest land in the US, caused by a volcanic eruption
10. This park has the deepest lake in the United States
11. This color shows up in the name of a National Park in California
12. This National Park deserves a gold medal

Answers: Where National Park Will You Go Next?

1. Zion
2. Big Bend
3. Glacier
4. Olympic
5. Sequoia
6. Bryce
7. Mesa Verde
8. Biscayne
9. Wind Cave
10. Great Basin
11. Katmai
12. Yellowstone
13. Voyageurs
14. Arches
15. Badlands
16. Denali
17. Glacier Bay
18. Hot Springs

```
F  M  M  E  S  A  V  E  R  D  E  B  N  E  Y
E  A  B  I  G  B  E  N  D  E  S  A  S  E  M
Y  L  I  C  A  L  O  Y  N  E  E  D  L  T  G
D  M  G  A  S  S  A  U  C  N  R  L  U  E  R
C  E  L  I  I  T  S  C  R  E  O  A  A  K  E
S  N  A  W  Y  E  E  O  I  W  T  N  A  C  A
G  I  C  H  A  A  Q  C  S  E  M  D  N  S  T
N  O  I  Z  P  R  U  T  I  M  R  S  N  E  B
I  W  E  L  M  P  O  N  B  W  E  B  K  H  A
R  J  R  F  D  N  I  F  L  I  H  B  U  C  S
P  A  B  E  E  S  A  N  E  S  O  P  W  R  I
S  J  A  E  N  Y  A  C  S  I  B  A  U  A  N
T  C  Y  I  A  D  O  H  H  Y  M  E  A  L  R
O  T  A  T  L  M  L  E  S  E  G  R  W  R  J
H  S  T  O  I  K  A  T  M  A  I  R  O  P  B
I  C  H  U  R  C  O  L  Y  M  P  I  C  O  U
O  Y  G  T  S  D  E  O  S  B  R  Y  C  E  T
W  I  N  D  C  A  V  E  I  N  R  O  H  E  M
```

Little Bison Press is an independent children's book publisher based in the Pacific Northwest. We promote exploration, conservation, and adventure through our books. Established in 2021, our passion for outside spaces and travel inspired the creation of Little Bison Press.

We seek to publish books that support children in learning about and caring for the natural places in our world.

To learn more, visit:

www.littlebisonpress.com

Want more free games and activities? Visit our website!